Key Stage 2

Reading and Writing Fiction

Carol Matchett

Name _Isha_

Schofield & Sims

Introduction

Everyone loves reading a good story. There is nothing better than losing yourself in an adventure, discovering an amazing fictional world or sharing the experiences of your favourite character.

This book will help you to get the most out of the stories that you read and will show you how to appreciate their best features. The book includes many extracts from well-known stories, which will help you to understand how these features work. It also gives you ideas for developing and improving your own stories – so that others will love reading them!

Finding your way around this book

Before you start using this book, write your name in the name box on the first page. Then decide how to begin. If you want a complete course on reading and writing fiction, you should work right through the book from beginning to end.

Another way to use the book is to dip into it when you want to find out about a particular topic. The Contents page will help you to find the pages you need. Whichever way you choose, don't try to do too much at once – it's better to work through the book in short bursts.

When you have found the topic you want to study, look out for these icons, which mark different parts of the text.

Activities

This icon shows you the activities that you should complete – you write in the spaces provided. This book does not include answers to the activities because there are so many different possible answers and it wouldn't be practical to list all of them. Check your answers with an adult and when you are sure that you understand the topic, put a tick in the box beside it on the Contents page. On page 32 you will find suggestions for some projects (**Now you try!**), which will give you even more opportunities to improve your understanding of reading and writing fiction.

Explanation

This text explains the topic and gives examples. Read it before you start the activities.

Notes

Some extra things that you need to know.

Information

This text gives you background information about the history of story writing. Surprise your friends with some fascinating facts!

Contents

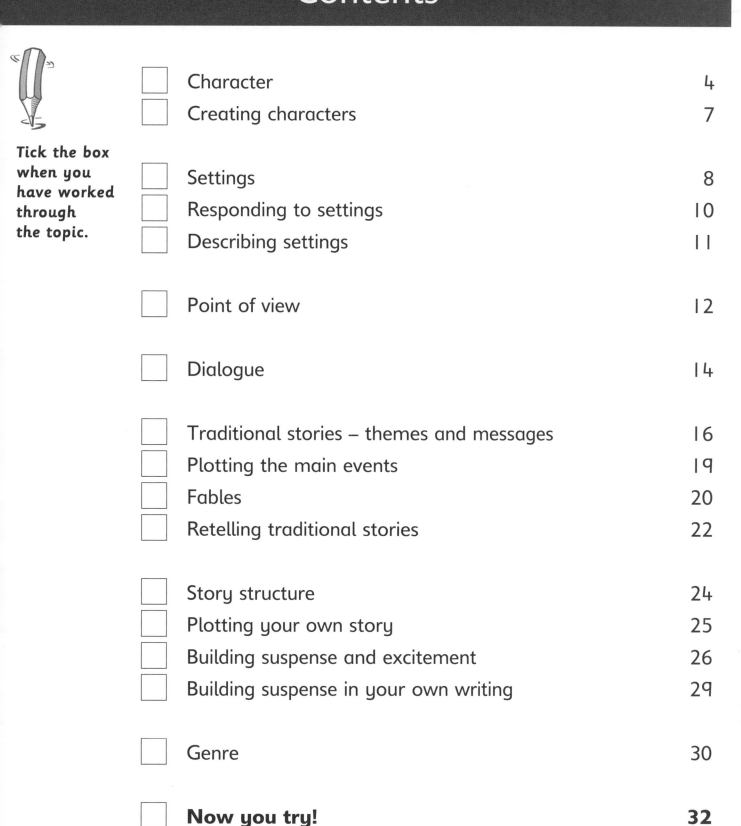

Tick the box when you have worked through the topic.

13 August

Character

Characters are the **people** that a story is about. A story can also have animals or imaginary creatures as characters. Sometimes we like the characters – sometimes we don't like them!

We learn about characters from how they are **described**, how they **behave**, what they **say** and what **others say** about them.

Scrooge is the main **character** in the story 'A Christmas Carol' by Charles Dickens. You are going to read some extracts from the beginning of the story that show how the character is introduced.

1. This is the author's **description** of Scrooge. Read it and think what it tells us about him.

> **A Christmas Carol**
>
> The cold within him froze his old features, nipped his pointed nose, shrivelled his cheek, stiffened his **gait**, made his eyes red, his thin lips blue, and spoke out in his grating voice. A frosty **rime** was on his head, and on his eyebrows, and his wiry chin. He carried his own low temperature always about with him ...
>
> **Adapted from A Christmas Carol by Charles Dickens**

notes
gait – walk.
rime – frost or ice.

2. a) Read the description again. Underline information about what he **looks like** in one colour and information about what **sort of person** he is in another colour.

b) Then draw a picture to show what you think he **looks like**.

3. Do you **like** or **dislike** Scrooge? Circle your answer and give a reason.

I | like | | dislike | Scrooge because

4. Here is an example of how Scrooge **behaves**.

> The door of Scrooge's counting-house was open so that he might keep an eye upon his clerk, who in a dismal little cell beyond was copying letters. Scrooge had a very small fire, but the clerk's fire was so very much smaller that it looked like one coal. But he couldn't **replenish** it, for Scrooge kept the coal-box in his own room ...
>
> **Adapted from *A Christmas Carol* by Charles Dickens**

replenish – build up again.

5. a) What does this tell us about Scrooge? Draw a circle round each of the **two** words that best complete the sentence below.

This behaviour shows us that Scrooge is

unhappy	mean	kind	unfeeling

b) Why did you choose these words to describe Scrooge?

_____

_____

6. Charles Dickens also writes these words, which show what other people thought about Scrooge.

> Nobody ever stopped him in the street to say, with gladsome looks, 'My dear Scrooge, how are you? When will you come to see me?'

What did **other people** think about him? Write your answer in the thought bubble.

7. Here is some **dialogue** that takes place just before Christmas. Underline the words spoken by **Scrooge** in one colour and the words spoken by **his nephew** in a different colour.

'A merry Christmas, uncle! God save you!' cried a cheerful voice. It was the voice of Scrooge's nephew...

'Bah!' said Scrooge, 'Humbug!'

He had so heated himself with rapid walking in the fog, this nephew of Scrooge's, that he was all in a glow; his face was **ruddy** and handsome and his eyes sparkled.

'Christmas a humbug, uncle!' said Scrooge's nephew. 'You don't mean that, I am sure?'

'I do,' said Scrooge. 'Merry Christmas! What reason have you to be merry? You're poor enough.'

'Come, then,' returned the nephew gaily. 'What reason have you to be **morose**? You're rich enough.'

Scrooge having no better answer ready on the spur of the moment, said 'Bah!' again; and followed it up with 'Humbug.'

'Don't be cross, uncle!' said the nephew.

'What else can I be,' returned the uncle, 'when I live in such a world of fools as this? What's Christmas time to you but a time for paying bills without money; a time for finding yourself a year older, and not an hour richer...'

Adapted from *A Christmas Carol* by Charles Dickens

ruddy – rosy, flushed.
morose – miserable.

---

8. Scrooge and his nephew have differing views of Christmas. Write below what each might say about it.

Scrooge < Christmas is

Christmas is

Scrooge's Nephew

Creating characters

When you are describing characters in your own stories, give your readers an idea of what **sort of people** the characters are – should we **like** them or **dislike** them? You can do this through **description**. For example, when Charles Dickens described Scrooge he wrote:

The cold within him froze his old features, nipped his pointed nose, shrivelled his cheek...

But when he described Scrooge's nephew, he wrote:

...he was all in a glow; his face was ruddy and handsome and his eyes sparkled.

1. Think of some words and phrases you could use to **describe** two characters – one who is pleasant, cheerful and likeable and one who is unpleasant. Add your ideas to this chart:

	Likeable character	**Unpleasant character**
Eyes	sparkling, laughing, twinkle	
Expression		
Way of speaking		
Way of walking or moving		

2. You meet the two characters in the street and say 'Good morning!' How would each character reply?

Likeable character	**Unpleasant character**

Settings

The **setting** of a story is **where** and **when** it takes place. Some stories are set in familiar places, such as a school or a house. Other stories are set in unfamiliar places – in the past, for example, or in an imaginary world.

Authors use **description** to give readers a **clear picture** of the setting. They might use a long **scene-setting description** or they might give **small details** about it as they go along.

1. Here is the opening to a story called 'The Selfish Giant' by Oscar Wilde. Read this section of the story and try to **picture the setting** that is described.

The Selfish Giant

Every afternoon, as they were coming from school, the children used to go and play in the Giant's garden.

It was a large lovely garden, with soft green grass. Here and there over the grass stood beautiful flowers like stars, and there were 12 peach trees that in the springtime broke out into delicate blossoms of pink and pearl, and in the autumn bore rich fruit. The birds sat on the trees and sang so sweetly that the children used to stop their games in order to listen to them. 'How happy we are here!' they cried to each other.

Adapted from 'The Selfish Giant' by Oscar Wilde

---

2. Draw in the box the setting as you picture it. Then go back and read the passage again and underline the words and phrases that helped you to picture the garden.

The Giant's Garden in Springtime

Settings

The story then describes what happens when the Giant scares the children away and builds a high wall round the garden to keep them out.

Then the Spring came ... only in the garden of the Selfish Giant it was still winter.

The birds did not care to sing in it, and the trees forgot to blossom. Once a beautiful flower put its head out from the grass, but it was so sorry for the children that it slipped back into the ground again, and went off to sleep.

The only people who were pleased were the Snow and Frost. 'Spring has forgotten this garden,' they cried, 'so we will live here all the year round.' The snow covered up the grass with her great white cloak, and the frost painted all the trees silver. Then they invited the North Wind to stay with them, and he came. He roared all day about the garden and blew the chimney-pots down. ...Then Hail came. Every day for three hours he rattled on the roof of the castle till he broke most of the slates, and then he ran round and round the garden as fast as he could...

Adapted from 'The Selfish Giant' by Oscar Wilde

3. Draw a picture to show what the Giant's garden looks like now. Label the picture with words and phrases from the description.

+--+
| **The Giant's Garden Now** |
| |
| |
| |
| |
| |
| |
| |
| |
| |
+--+

You can find the story 'The Selfish Giant' in *The Happy Prince and Other Stories* by Oscar Wilde. Why not read the whole story and find out what happens?

Responding to settings

Descriptions of settings make you **feel** something about a place or what might happen there. For example, a frightening setting might make you expect something awful, and a magical setting might make you expect all sorts of amazing things. **Adjectives** and **similes** are important in helping us to respond to settings in this way.

1. Think about the two descriptions of the Giant's garden. How do they make you **feel**? Write your answers in the bubbles below.

a) Description 1 (page 8):

> This description makes me feel
>
> because

b) Description 2 (page 9):

> This description makes me feel
>
> because

2. **a)** Read again the first description of the garden (page 8). Find adjectives or words and phrases used to describe these items.

the grass	
the blossom	
the birds	

b) Read again the second description of the garden (page 9). What did these 'visitors' to the garden do?

the snow	
the frost	
the North Wind	
the hail	

Describing settings

When you are describing a setting you need to include enough **detail** to give your reader an exact picture of the place where the events take place. Choose words and phrases carefully, and remember that the **time of day** and the **weather** can also be part of the setting.

1. You are writing a story set in a **real place**, such as a playground, a shopping centre or a busy street. Fill in details about the setting to complete the description below.

It was _____ . There were _____

_____ . Here and there _____

_____

All around _____ . Close by

_____

_____

2. Now you are writing a story set in an **imaginary** place, such as a wizard's workshop, or another planet. Fill in details about the new setting to complete the description.

It was _____ . There were _____

_____ . Here and there _____

_____

All around _____ . Close by

_____

_____

Did you know...? One of the first stories set in an imaginary world was *Gulliver's Travels* by Jonathan Swift. It was first published in 1726. Gulliver, the hero, visits many strange worlds. The most famous is the island of Lilliput, where all the people are tiny and Gulliver is like a giant. Other imaginary worlds that Gulliver visits in the story include Brobdingnag, where the people are as tall as steeples, and the amazing flying island of Laputa.

Point of view

Stories can be told from different **points of view**. 'Point of view' varies depending on who is telling the story and through whose eyes we see the events.

Some stories are told in the **first person**, as if one of the characters is telling the story. Other stories are written in the **third person**, as if someone else is telling us about what happened to the characters. Even if a story is written in the third person, we might still follow the events through the eyes of one particular character as we are told about his or her thoughts and feelings.

1. Here is an extract from the start of a story. See if you can work out **who** is telling the story, and underline the clues that show you who it is.

> ### 1: Monday
>
> Okay, okay. So hang me. I killed the bird. For pity's sake, I'm a cat. It's practically my *job* to go creeping round the garden after sweet little eensy-weensy birdy-pies that can hardly fly from one hedge to another. So what am I supposed to do when one of the poor feathery little flutterballs just throws itself into my mouth? I mean, it practically landed on my paws. It could have *hurt* me.
>
> Okay, okay. So I biffed it. Is that any reason for Ellie to cry in my fur so hard I almost drown and squeeze me so hard I almost choke?
>
> 'Ow Tuffy!' she says, all sniffles and red eyes and piles of wet tissues. 'Ow Tuffy. How could you do that?'
>
> How could I do that? I'm a cat. How did I know there was going to be such a giant great fuss...
>
> **From *The Diary of a Killer Cat* by Anne Fine**

The story is being told by:

Point of view

2. Ellie's version of these events might be very different from the version you have just read. Write Ellie's diary for the same day. Remember to look for clues about Ellie's reaction in the diary extract shown on page 12.

Ellie's Diary – 1: Monday

_____

_____

_____

_____

_____

_____

_____

_____

_____

3. What do you learn about the character of Tuffy from the extract on page 12?

_____

_____

_____

Did you know...? Many of the very early novels, written in the eighteenth century, were written as if they were diaries, journals or accounts written by the main character. Some people say that _Robinson Crusoe_ by Daniel Defoe (published in 1719) was the first English novel. It describes the adventures of a man shipwrecked on a desert island and is written as if Robinson Crusoe himself is telling the story.

Dialogue

Dialogue is the conversation that takes place between two or more characters in a story. It is an important part of many stories because it gives us information about the **characters** and tells us about **what is happening** or about to happen. Dialogue is sometimes used as an interesting way of **opening a story**.

I. Here is a section of dialogue taken from the **opening of a story**. There are four **characters** involved. Use a different colour to underline the words spoken by each one.

Little Women

'It's so dreadful to be poor!' sighed Meg, looking down at her old dress.

'I don't think it's fair for some girls to have plenty of pretty things, and other girls nothing at all,' added little Amy, with an injured sniff.

'We've got Father and Mother and each other,' said Beth, contentedly, from her corner.

The four young faces on which the firelight shone brightened at the cheerful words, but darkened again as Jo said sadly:

'We haven't got Father, and shall not have him for a long time.' She didn't say 'perhaps never' but each silently added it, thinking of Father far away, where the fighting was.

Adapted from Little Women by Louisa May Alcott

---

2. a) What do we learn about the four **characters** from this dialogue?

_____

_____

_____

b) What do we learn about **the problems they have** as the story begins?

_____

_____

Dialogue

When reading dialogue, always remember that *how* the words are spoken is just as important as **what is said**. For example:

muttered   screamed   whispered anxiously   said with a sigh

These words and phrases help to suggest the **thoughts** and **feelings** of the character.

3. Read again the dialogue on page 14. Circle the words and phrases that show *how* the words are spoken.

a) What does this suggest about the **mood** and **feelings** of the characters?

_____

_____

_____

b) Which of the characters seems the most cheerful? How can you tell?

seems the most cheerful because _____

_____

4. Sort these phrases into the right box, according to the **feelings** they show. One is done for you.

~~giggled Jill~~   sobbed the child   the King said with a smile
replied angrily   she said with a frown   grinned Leo
added the old man, in a cheerful voice   scowled the Princess
he said, laughing merrily   with a heavy sigh

Happy	**Unhappy**
giggled Jill	

Traditional stories – themes and messages

Traditional stories were first told a long time ago. They feature **traditional characters** such as kings, princes and princesses and farmers, and traditional **settings**, such as woods, strange lands and castles. Traditional stories often have a familiar **theme** or **message**, which is made clear when 'good' characters are rewarded or 'bad' characters are punished.

1. Here is a traditional story. As you read it, think about whether the King is a 'good' or a 'bad' character.

The Magic Bottle

Long ago there lived a wealthy King. Because he was so rich and powerful, people were always giving him wonderful gifts. One of these gifts was a small bluey-green bottle containing a magic liquid – just one drop would keep a dying man alive. As you might guess, the King guarded the bottle carefully.

One day, the court was saddened to hear that the most gallant of all the King's knights was dying. In his youth this man had been a soldier, who fought bravely in many great battles. He was respected by everyone. Now he was old and dying. His only wish was to stay alive a little longer to see the birth of his first grandchild.

'Just one drop of the magic liquid would save him,' the court doctor told the King.
'Certainly not!' replied the King, 'This precious liquid is meant for someone special.'
The doctor did not dare to argue with the King.

A short time later a young servant who worked for the King was badly injured when falling from his horse. The young man was popular and everyone was disturbed by the news.

'He is so young,' pleaded the Queen, 'He is the same age as our own son. Just one drop of the magic liquid would save him.'

'Certainly not!' replied the King, 'This precious liquid is meant for someone important.'

Even the Queen could not argue with the King.

A few years later the King's chief adviser and closest friend became very ill. Gathering all his strength, the man went to visit the King to ask for one drop of the magic liquid from the bluey-green bottle. But the King refused even him.

The years passed and the bluey-green bottle remained unused. One day the King himself was taken ill. The King's condition became worse and worse and the doctors did not know what to do. Eventually, the King ordered his servant to bring him the bluey-green bottle.

When the servant returned, the King grabbed the bottle. He pulled out the cork. He put the bottle to his lips, expecting to taste the magic liquid that would save his life ... but there was nothing. There was nothing in the bottle!

You see, the bottle had been left for so long that the magic liquid had all dried up! With a terrible sigh, the King died. The magic liquid, guarded for so long, had saved no-one, not even the King. And what about the bottle? Well, that was kept and put on display to remind everyone of what had happened.

Adapted from a European folk tale

2. a) Do you think the King is a 'good' character or a 'bad' character? Circle your answer:

good		bad

b) Give reasons for your answer:

_____

_____

_____

3. Circle the words that you think best describe the character of the King:

caring	mean	selfish	generous

wise	foolish	kind

4. What is the **theme** or **message** of the story 'The Magic Bottle' (see pages 16 and 17)?

_____

_____

_____

5. Find examples of these **traditional story features** in the story.

Traditional story features	Examples in 'The Magic Bottle'
Traditional characters	The main character is a King.
Traditional setting	
Magical event or magical object	
Good characters rewarded or bad characters punished	
A message or theme	

Did you know... Traditional stories were originally told rather than written down. Centuries ago, people would gather round to hear the tales of the storyteller, which included myths, legends and events from history. The same stories were told and retold for hundreds of years before anyone thought to write them down.

Plotting the main events

The **plot** of a story is the series of **events** that take place. Sometimes the plot is very simple and straightforward; sometimes there are complications. You can use a **flowchart** like the one below to plot the **main events** in a story.

1. Here is a **flowchart** for you to plot the **main events** in the story 'The Magic Bottle' (pages 16 and 17). The first three events have been filled in already: you need to fill in the rest.

> The King had a bottle of magic liquid that could keep people alive.

▼

> One day, one of the King's knights was dying.

▼

> The King would not give him any of the magic liquid.

▼

> A short time later,

▼

>

▼

>

▼

>

▼

>

Fables

A fable is one kind of **traditional story**. It tends to be short and often ends with a **moral**. The moral tells us what we should learn from the story – particularly how to avoid making the same mistakes as the characters. The characters in a fable are often **animals** – but they behave just like humans!

1. Read this fable about a dog. Think what the **moral** of the story might be.

The Dog and the Bone

A dog sniffing round the back of the butcher's stall had found a juicy piece of meat. As he trotted home, carrying the meat in his mouth, he looked forward to devouring it.

Soon the dog reached a stream with a plank laid across it, to help people cross. As he was crossing the stream he looked down and saw his own reflection in the water. Thinking it was another dog, with another piece of meat, he made up his mind to have that piece of meat as well as his own. 'What a feast I will have!' he thought.

The dog made a sudden grab for the meat reflected in the water. But as soon as he opened his mouth his own piece of meat fell out, disappearing into the water – never to be seen again. And so the dog went home hungry.

2. Which of these **morals** best fits this story? Make your choice and write it in the box below.

- Don't put off until tomorrow what you can do today.
- Slow and steady wins the day.
- Don't go chasing dreams: be satisfied with what you have.
- If at first you don't succeed, try, try and try again.

Moral

3. The dog is **foolish** and makes a **big mistake**. What might he be thinking at the end of the story?

I feel

I wish I had

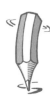

4. Think of an idea for another **fable** featuring the **character** of the foolish dog.

Here is the **moral** for your story. **Moral:** **Look before you leap.**

In the box below, write about what the dog might do to show that this moral is true.

Did you know... The story of 'The Dog and the Bone' was first told hundreds of years ago. Many people believe that the original teller of the story was a man called Aesop, who lived in Greece in the sixth century BC. He made up lots of fables, which have been popular ever since. A version of *Aesop's Fables* was one of the first printed books in Britain: printed in 1484 by William Caxton, it included illustrations made using wooden printing blocks.

Retelling traditional stories

Sometimes when people **retell traditional stories** they bring the story up to date. The **plot** is the same, but details about the **setting**, **characters** and **events** are changed to make the story more modern.

I. Here is a modern version of the traditional story 'The Old Woman and the Vinegar Bottle'. As you read, underline the clues that show this is a modern version of the story.

> ### Carrie and her Wishes
>
> Carrie was feeling very pleased with herself as she sat down on the stripy sofa. It had been a hard day, but here she was at last in her new home. Yes, it was a bit of a mess at the moment. And yes, it needed a lick of paint... but it was hers.
>
>
>
> Over the next few weeks Carrie spent all her spare time working on the flat. When she had finished she was delighted. She e-mailed all her friends, inviting them over.
>
> One day, Carrie was asked to deliver a parcel to a lovely new house in a rather grand street. It had a gravel driveway, a double garage, a beautiful garden ... and a swimming pool. Carrie thought of her tiny little flat and then thought about this beautiful house. 'It's so unfair,' she said to herself, 'I wish I could live in a beautiful house like this with a gravel driveway and a swimming pool.'
>
> Now it just so happened that the Lottery Fairy heard this wish and with a puff of smoke, a scattering of stars and a few magic words Carrie found herself living in the beautiful new house!
>
> Carrie was really pleased. She invited all her friends over. They had barbecues in the garden and swam in the pool.

One day, Carrie was reading a magazine article about a film star. There were photographs of the star posing at her home – a beautiful mansion with a huge swimming pool, a gym and a landing space for her private helicopter. Carrie thought about her own house with its tiny little swimming pool, 'It's so unfair. I wish I could live in a mansion.'

It just so happened that the Lottery Fairy was again passing by. With a puff of smoke, a scattering of stars and a few magic words, Carrie found herself living in the film star's mansion. Carrie was delighted. She held parties every night so that she could show off her amazing mansion. Of course, she no longer invited her old friends – they were not grand enough.

One evening at one of her parties, Carrie overheard one guest telling another about a palace belonging to a Prince. 'It has 78 rooms – and all so grand!' Carrie thought of her mansion with its 24 rooms and then thought about the Prince's palace with 78 grand rooms: 'It's so unfair. I wish I could live in a palace, with everything grand and regal.'

Now it just so happened that the Lottery Fairy was again passing by. With a puff of smoke, a scattering of stars and a few magic words Carrie found herself living in a palace.

Carrie was overjoyed. She held grand balls and everything seemed wonderful. But on the days when there was no ball, no-one visited. The servants were scared to speak to her. Her old friends had long since forgotten her, as she had never replied to their texts. Soon Carrie became lonely in her 78-room palace. She began to think about how happy she had once been in her little one bedroom flat.

Now it just so happened that the Lottery Fairy had had quite enough of Carrie and her wishes. So with a great cloud of smoke, a huge thunderbolt and a few rather angry magic words, Carrie found herself sitting on her old stripy sofa back in her old flat.

Story structure

The **structure** of a story is the **shape** of the story, showing how it is built up through the sequence of events. 'Carrie and her Wishes' (pages 22 and 23) is a **circle story** because the story starts and ends in the same place.

1. The first three events in the story 'Carrie and her Wishes' have already been written on the flowchart below. Complete the flowchart to show the circular plot.

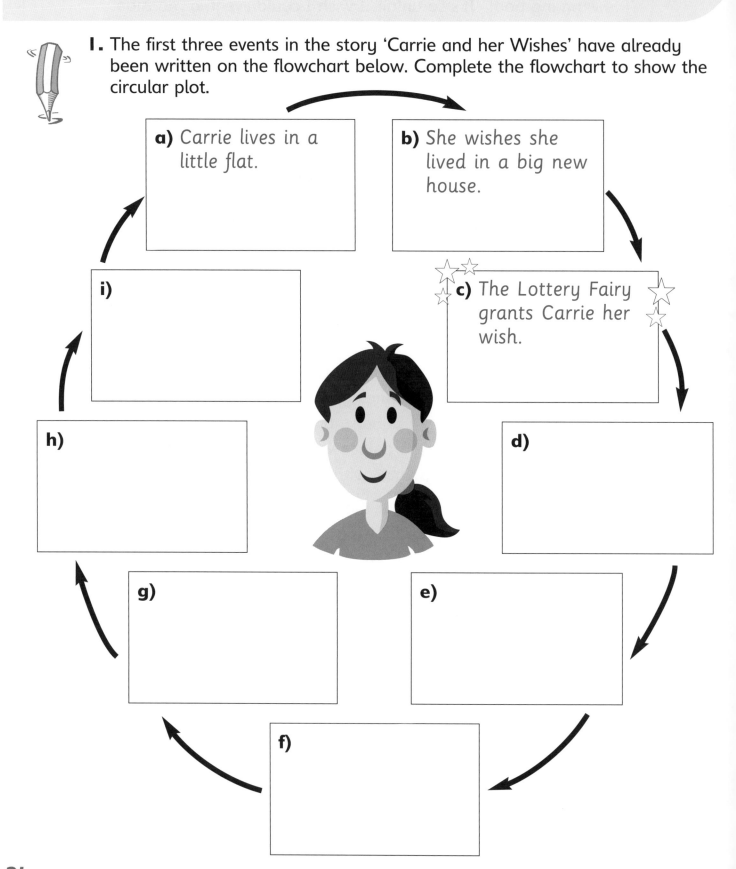

a) Carrie lives in a little flat.

b) She wishes she lived in a big new house.

c) The Lottery Fairy grants Carrie her wish.

d)

e)

f)

g)

h)

i)

Plotting your own story

1. Make up your own **circle story** based on 'Carrie and her Wishes' (pages 22 and 23). Keep the same idea of someone who keeps wishing for something better, but change the main **character** and the things that he or she wishes for. Plot the main events of your story on this flowchart to show the circular plot.

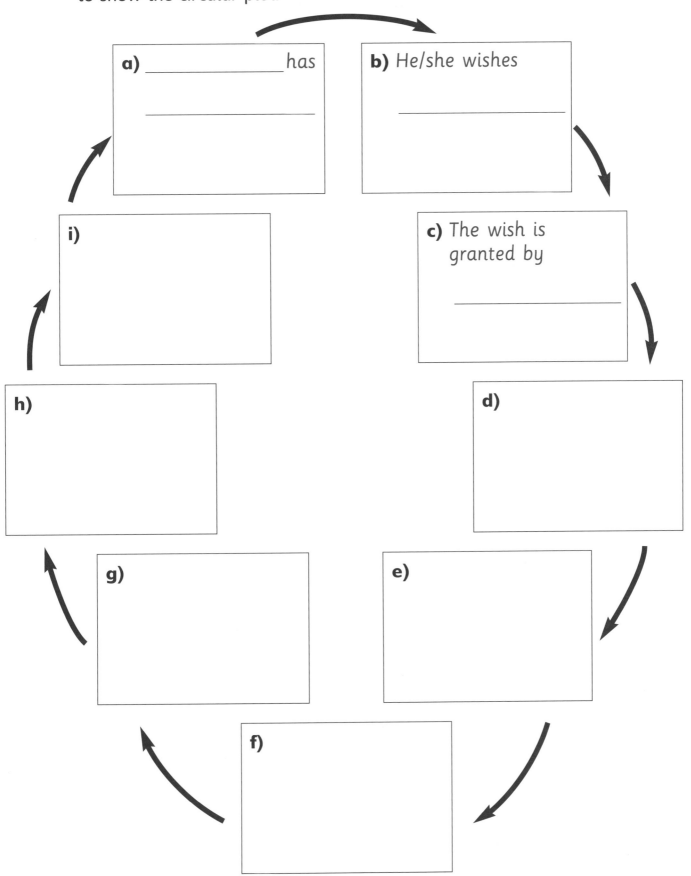

a) _____ has
_____

b) He/she wishes
_____

c) The wish is granted by
_____

d)

e)

f)

g)

h)

i)

Building suspense and excitement

Writers build **suspense** and **excitement** through the way they tell the story. Suspense **builds up** through a series of events, leaving you expecting something to happen at any moment. **Descriptive language** and the careful **choice of words** help to build the excitement.

1. Here is an extract from *The Wind in the Willows* by Kenneth Grahame. In this part of the story, Mole has entered the Wild Wood against the advice of his friend the Rat. As you read the extract, put a score for Mole's fear factor in each of the boxes, using the scale below.

1 = not too frightened; 2 = a little bit frightened; 3 = frightened; 4 = very frightened; 5 = extremely frightened.

The Wild Wood

There was nothing to alarm him at first entry. Twigs crackled under his feet, logs tripped him, funguses on stumps resembled caricatures, and startled him, but that was all fun and exciting. It led him on to where the light was less, and trees crouched nearer, and holes made ugly mouths at him.

Everything was very still now. The dusk advanced on him steadily, rapidly, gathering in behind and before; and the light seemed to be draining away like floodwater.

Then the faces began.

Fear factor ☐

It was over his shoulder, and indistinctly, that he first thought he saw a face: a little evil face, looking out at him from a hole. When he confronted it, the thing had vanished.

He quickened his pace, telling himself cheerfully not to begin imagining things. He passed another hole, and another, and another; and then – yes! – no! – yes! Certainly a little narrow face, with hard eyes, had flashed up for an instant from a hole, and was gone. Then suddenly every hole, far and near seemed to possess its face, all fixing on him glances of hatred: all hard eyed and evil and sharp.

If he could only get away from the holes in the banks, he thought, there would be no more faces. He swung off the path and plunged into the untrodden places of the wood.

Then the whistling began.

Fear factor ☐

Building suspense and excitement

Very faint and shrill it was, and far behind him, when he first heard it; but somehow it made him hurry forward. Then, still very faint and shrill, it sounded far ahead of him, and made him hesitate and want to go back. As he halted in indecision it broke out on either side, and seemed to be passed on throughout the whole length of the wood to its farthest limit. They were up and alert and ready, whoever they were! And he – he was alone, and unarmed, and far from any help; and the night was closing in.

Then the pattering began.   *Fear factor* ☐

He thought it was only falling leaves at first, so slight was the sound of it. Then as it grew it took on a regular rhythm, and he knew it for the pat-pat-pat of little feet, a very long way off. Was it in front or behind? It seemed to be first one, then the other, then both. It grew and it multiplied, till from every quarter it seemed to be closing in on him.

The pattering increased till it sounded like sudden hail on the dry-leaf carpet spread around him. The whole wood seemed to be running now, running hard, hunting, chasing, closing in round something or – somebody?

In panic, he began to run too, aimlessly, he knew not whither. He ran up against things, he fell over things and into things, and he darted under things and dodged round things. At last he took refuge in the dark deep hollow of an old beech tree, which offered shelter, concealment – perhaps even safety?

Fear factor ☐

And as he lay there panting and trembling, and listened to the whistlings and the patterings outside, he knew it at last, in all its fullness, that dread thing which other little dwellers in field and hedgerow had encountered here, and known as their darkest moment – that thing which the Rat had vainly tried to shield him from – the Terror of the Wild Wood!

Adapted from *The Wind in the Willows* by Kenneth Grahame

Building suspense and excitement

Writers build suspense and excitement in many different ways. They use **descriptive language** to tell us about sounds and feelings. They create **doubt** and ask **questions** that make us wonder what might happen. They sometimes use **repeated phrases** to draw us in and build up the tension.

2. Read again 'The Wild Wood' (pages 26 and 27). Underline words and phrases that help to **build suspense and excitement** in each part of the extract.

3. Look for examples of where these techniques were used in the passage. Write some examples in the boxes below.

Technique	Examples
Descriptive language (including similes and metaphors)	*holes made ugly mouths at him*
Doubts (is something real, or is it just imagined?)	*When he turned and confronted it, the thing had vanished*
Repeated words or phrases	
Questions that make us wonder	

Building suspense in your own writing

When writing your own stories, remember to **build excitement** and **suspense** at the most important point in the story. Think how other authors do this and try to use some of the same ideas in your own writing. **Start quietly** and **build up** to the most exciting moment. Use description, questions or repeated phrases to draw the reader in.

1. Imagine that a character in your story is in a dark place. It is late at night. Something terrible is going to happen – but what ... and when? Decide how you might build up the **suspense**. Make notes of ideas, words and phrases that you might use.

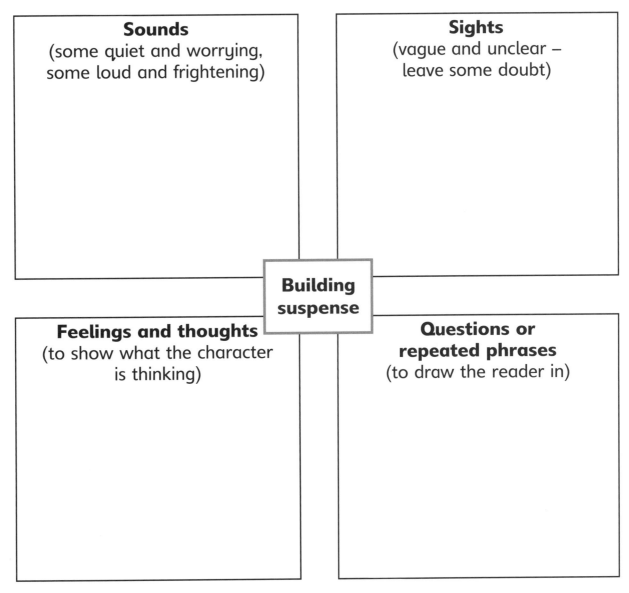

Sounds
(some quiet and worrying, some loud and frightening)

Sights
(vague and unclear – leave some doubt)

Building suspense

Feelings and thoughts
(to show what the character is thinking)

Questions or repeated phrases
(to draw the reader in)

2. Use your ideas to write this part of the story on a separate piece of paper.

Genre

There are many different types, or **genre**, of story: adventure stories, mysteries, fantasy and science fiction are just a few. Each of these story types has special features – plots, characters, settings and themes that you recognise.

For example, if you were to read a story described as a **ghost story**, you would expect it to be set in a spooky place. You would expect tension, surprises and something to frighten the main characters.

1. Here are some **story genres**.

adventure	mystery	science fiction
fantasy world	realistic	ghost story

Read the blurb on the back of these books and decide which **genre** each book belongs to. Write the genre on the label. Underline the clues in the blurb that told you the genre.

a)

A series of robberies... a strange light on the beach... What is happening at Sunnyways Hotel? Who is responsible for the thefts?

Zoë and Mick set out to investigate in:
The Case of the Missing Diamonds.

b)

'It was Meena's fault.' 'Meena did it, not me!' That was all Meena ever heard these days. Ever since Malik had come to live with them everything was Meena's fault. And Dad always believed Malik, not her. That was the worst thing of all.

c)

On a mission to the planet Alpha III the spaceship Crusader comes under attack from an alien vessel. Can the crew escape through a black hole? Or will they be captured by an alien life force?

d)

With a treasure map found in an old book, Jason Brown sets off on an action-packed search for lost treasure. The map will take him across four continents and bring him face to face with the evil Professor Claw and many other villains ...

e)

A sinister house ...
A scream in the night ...
No wonder Kelly is having nightmares. But are they nightmares ... or are those events real?

f)

Kuldip Singh steps through a doorway and finds himself in the strange world of Talavon. The forest people of Talavon live in fear of the evil Emperor. Can Kuldip help them? And can he find his way back to the real world?

Did you know...?

The genre of science fiction ('sci-fi') began at the end of the nineteenth century. H. G. Wells was the first sci-fi writer. He wrote stories about invasions from outer space (*The War of the Worlds*) and time travel (*The Time Machine*). These themes have been used many times since in other science fiction stories.

Now you try!

Here are some projects that you can try at home to make you think more about stories.

Reading challenge

We all have our favourite sort of books – perhaps you love ghost stories or adventures. Next time you are choosing a book at school or at the library, why not set yourself the challenge of reading a book from a **different genre** – something you wouldn't usually choose.

TV watch

It is not only books that tell stories – so do drama serials and the 'soaps' on television. Each one has **characters**, **a setting**, **a plot** ... just like the stories you read in books. Next time you are watching your favourite TV programme, think about what makes it a good story. Why are the characters popular? Why do you keep watching? What makes the story work?

Book club

Start a book club for your friends or family. Get everyone in your book club to read the same book and then you can all talk about it at your meeting. Or you could ask all the members of the book club to bring along their favourite book to recommend to the rest of the group.

Drama

A rainy day is the ideal time for acting out a story. Don't choose a story that is too complicated – a **traditional story** that everyone knows is ideal.

Storytelling

One of the best ways of learning to write really good stories is to try *telling* your story to someone. Try entertaining a younger brother or sister or friend by telling a story. See if you can keep the person interested by using different ways of **building up** the story and making it **exciting**.

Chain stories

This is a fun way of writing stories. You can try it on a long journey. Write the **opening** of a story. Leave it at an interesting point and then pass the story on to a friend or another member of the family. Ask him or her to write the next part of the story and then pass it back to you. You carry on the story and then pass it on again – until someone thinks of a good **ending**!